Ryburn V
Lea

CU00864932

F/RIC 1.1
21950

Ransom Neutron Stars
Shopping with Zombies
by Stephen Rickard
Illustrated by Richard Williams

Published by Ransom Publishing Ltd.
Unit 7, Brocklands Farm, West Meon, Hampshire GU32 1JN, UK
www.ransom.co.uk

ISBN   978 178591 438 6
First published in 2017
Reprinted 2018

There is a reading comprehension quiz available for this book in the popular
Accelerated Reader® software system. For information about ATOS, Accelerated
Reader, quiz points and reading levels please visit www.renaissance.com. Accelerated
Reader, AR, the Accelerated Reader Logo, and ATOS are trademarks of Renaissance
Learning, Inc. and its subsidiaries, registered common law or applied for in the U.S.
and other countries. Used under license.

Shopping with Zombies

Stephen Rickard

Illustrated by Richard Williams

Ransom

I went shopping with Dad.

"Can you get some milk?"
said Dad.

I picked up some milk.
I put it in the basket.

"We need some bread.
Can you get some bread?"
said Dad.

I picked up some bread.
I put it in the basket.

"I will get some cheese," said Dad.

Dad picked up some cheese and he put it in the basket.

"Can you get some juice?"
said Dad.

I picked up some juice
and I put it in the basket.

"We need some apples,"
I said.

"Can you get some apples, Dad?"

The basket was full.

"We need to pay,"
said Dad.

"You can pay,"
I said.

"I am the undead.
The undead hate shopping."

Have you read?

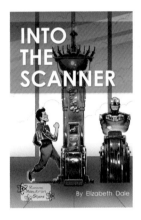

Into the Scanner

by Elizabeth Dale

Planting My Garden

by Stephen Rickard

Have you read?

Free Runners

by Alice Hemming

My Toys

by Stephen Rickard

Ransom Neutron Stars

Shopping with Zombies
Word count **118**

Red Book Band

Phonics

Phonics 1   Not Pop, Not Rock
Go to the Laptop Man
Gus and the Tin of Ham

Phonics 2   Deep in the Dark Woods
Night Combat
Ben's Jerk Chicken Van

Phonics 3   GBH
Steel Pan Traffic Jam
Platform 7

Phonics 4   The Rock Show
Gaps in the Brain
New Kinds of Energy

Book bands

Pink   Curry!
Free Runners
My Toys

Red   **Shopping with Zombies**
Into the Scanner
Planting My Garden

Yellow   Fit for Love
The Lottery Ticket
In the Stars

Blue   Awesome ATAs
Wolves
The Giant Jigsaw

Green   Fly, May FLY!
How to Start Your Own
Crazy Cult
The Care Home

Orange   Text Me
The Last Soldier
Best Friends